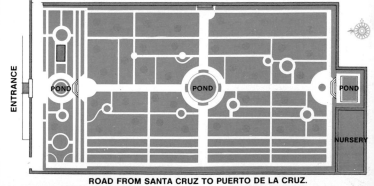

ROAD FROM SANTA CRUZ TO PUERTO DE LA CRUZ.

FLOWERS
IN THE
CANARY
ISLANDS

Translation: Bénédict School
Photographs: Author
Cover photograph: AGE FotoStock
Cover Design: Alfredo Anievas
Layout: María Casas

© Juan Alberto Rodríguez Pérez
Edited by EDITORIAL EVEREST, S. A.
Ctra. León-La Coruña, km 5 - LEÓN
ISBN: 84-241-4969-6
Legal deposit: LE. 671-1990
Printed in Spain

EDITORIAL EVERGRÁFICAS, S. A.
Ctra. León-La Coruña, km 5
LEÓN (Spain)

JUAN ALBERTO RODRIGUEZ PEREZ
Doctor in Biological Sciences (Botany) and T. Engineer in
Hortofruticulture and Gardening. Prof. of Gardening and
Landscaping Agricultural Technical Engineers College (La
Laguna). Ex-Curator of the Plant Acclimatization Garden of La
Orotava (Puerto de la Cruz).

FLOWERS IN THE CANARY ISLANDS

EDITORIAL EVEREST, S. A.

MADRID • LEON • BARCELONA • SEVILLA • GRANADA • VALENCIA
ZARAGOZA • LAS PALMAS DE GRAN CANARIA • LA CORUÑA
PALMA DE MALLORCA • ALICANTE – MEXICO • BUENOS AIRES

INTRODUCTION

The great acceptance of my last work, "The Exotic Flora of the Canary Islands", *including a great part of the palms, trees and exotic shrubs grown in the archipelago's gardens, has motivated me to write this book dealing with the most interesting vivacious and climbing plants grown in the Canaries, as well as some shrubby and arboreal species not included in the previously mentioned work.*

The plants described come from mainly the tropical and subtropical zones of the world. There are ones from Mexico such as the blue palm (Brahea armata) *and the gold cup* (Solandra maxima); *from islands in the Pacific such as the acalifa* (Acalpha wilkesiana) *and the pompadour* (Breynia disticha); *from Brazil such as the bougainvillia* (Bougainvillea spectabilis), *the parchita or purple granadilla* (Passiflora edulis) *and the flame vine* (Pyrostegia venusta); *from South Africa such as the strelitzia or bird of paradise flower* (Strelitzia reginae), *the coral tree* (Erythrina caffra) *and the Kafir lily* (Clivia miniata); *from Australia such as the umbrella tree* (Brassaia actinophylla), *from India such as the tamarind* (Tamarindus indica)*

The species are arranged in alphabetical order by their scientific names. The description of each includes its scientific name, the family it belongs to, its geographical distribution, common name, morphological characteristics, growing conditions, how it is used by man and in gardening, its flowering season and way of propagation. The data on flowering are from Puerto de la Cruz (Tenerife).

At the end of the book there is a glossary to facilitate comprehension of the botanical terms by those who are not familiar with them.

I thank my wife, Maija Riitta Rytkönen, for her collaboration in preparing this book.

Acalypha hispida Burm. f. Europhorbiaceae. Malasian archipelago.

CHENILLE PLANT

Evergreen shrub, dioecious, up to 4.5 m high. Leaves simple, alternate, green. broadly ovate, acuminate, serrate, up to 23 cm long. Small reddish flowers, grouped in pendulous spikes up to 40 cm long or more. Fruits in capsules.

Not particular about the soil. It can live in bright sunlight in a dry, warm place as well as in a damp one partially in the shade. Fast growing.

In gardening it is planted individually or in groups. Also in flower pots.

Flowering: Nearly year round.
Propagation: By seed, cuttings and air layering.

Acalypha wilkesiana Müll. Arg. Euphosbiaceae. Pacific Islands.

COPPER-LEAF

Monoecious, evergreen shrub, up to 4.5 m high. Leaves alternate, simple, ovate or elliptical, acuminate, serrate, greenish bronze in colour, mottled with red, copper or purple, up to 20 cm long or more. Small flowers in reddish spikes up to 10 cm long. Fruits in capsules.

Cv. Obovata. Leaves obovate, emarginated, with pink margins.

Tolerates most soils, preferring sunny spots although it withstands partial shade. Fast growing.

It is used in gardening individually, in groups and for hedges.

Propagation: Usually by cuttings.

Agapanthus praecox Willd. **ssp. orientalis (Leighton) Leighton**
[Agapanthus orientalis Leighton]. Liliaceae. South Africa.

COMMON AGAPANTHUS

Perennial herbaceous plant, rhizomatous. Leaves basal, strap-shaped, arched, up to 60 cm long and 6.5 cm wide. Blue flowers grouped in an umbel containing up to 110 flowers. Funnel-shaped corolla up to 5 cm in diameter. With a floral scape up to 105 cm long. Fruits in capsules.

Prefers rich soil and abundant water. Can live in bright sun as well as in shade.

Used in gardening to make up groups. It can also be planted in flower pots and the flowers used as cut flowers.

Flowering: Spring-summer.
Propagation: By seeds and division.

8

Allamanda cathartica L. **Cv. Hendersonii.** Apocynaceae.

GOLDEN TRUMPET

A woody, climbing plant, evergreen. Leaves opposite or in verticils with 3-4, entire, coriaceous, oblanceolate to elliptical-oblong, up to 12 cm long; dark green, glossy above and paler beneath. Hermaphrodite flowers, grouped in cymes with few flowers. Funnel-shaped corolla, yellow in colour with brown striation on the inside, pentalobate, up to 8 cm long and 8 cm in diameter. The flower buds appear dyed with brown. Fruits in globate, spiny capsules.

It accepts most soils. Needs a sunny location, abundant water and an appropriate fertilization for better flowering. Slow growing. Sensitive to frost. Resistant to drought.

In gardening it is used to cover walls, pergolas, etc. and also in pots.

Flowering: Summer-autumn-early winter.
Propagation: By cuttings.

Allamanda neriifolia Hook. Apocynaceae. South America.

An evergreen shrub, sometimes with scandent branches, up to 1.5 m high. Leaves entire, in verticils of 2-5 leaves, elliptical or oblong, acuminate, up to 16 cm long. Very short petiole. Hermaphrodite flowers, clustered in sparsely flowered cymes. Funnel-shaped corolla, yellow in colour with yellow-reddish striation in the narrow part, up to 4 cm in diameter and about 5 cm long. Tube with a wide base. Fruits in globate, spiny capsules.

Little demanding about soil. It prefers a sunny location, abundant water and an appropriate fertilization to give good flowering. Slow growing. Resistant to drought.

Used in gardening to cover walls, etc. Also as a potted plant.

Flowering: Almost year-round.
Propagation: By seeds and cuttings.

Alpinia zerumbet (Pers.) B. L. Burtt et R. M. Sm [*A. speciosa* (J. C. Wendl.) K. Schum.]. Zingiberaceae. East Asia.

SHELLFLOWER

Perennial, herbaceous plant, rhizomatous, with numerous stems, up to 3.5 m high. Simple, lanceolate leaves with pubescent margins. Limbs up to 75 cm long and 15 cm wide. Sheathing petioles. Hermaphrodite flowers grouped in panicles pendulous at the end of the stems. Trilobate corolla, white with rosaceous tones at the tip. Labium-shaped staminode, yellow with spots and red striation, up to 5 cm long. Fruits in capsules.

It prefers rich soils with abundant moisture and a slightly shady location. The dry stems must be cut off at ground level in order to favour the budding of new sprouts.

Used in gardening to form groups.

Flowering: Nearly year-round.
Propagation: By seeds and division.

Araucaria bidwillii Hook. Araucariaceae. Australia.

BUNYA-BUNYA

Evergreen tree up to 40 m high, with verticillate branches and blackish bark. Leaves arranged in a spiral, flat, lanceolate, coriaceous, with a very pointed tip, up to 6.5 cm long and 1.5 wide. Large female cones up to 30 cm and 20 cm diameter, woody. Edible seeds.

It accepts most soils well. It prefers a sunny location. Resistant to sea mist. Tolerates frost.

Its wood is good quality.

Used in gardening, in large gardens and parks. Also as an indoor potted plant and for decorating patios.

Reproduction: By seed.

Arlstolochia gigantea Mart. et Zucc., not Hook. Aristolochiaceae.
  Brazil.

BIRTHWORT

Evergreen climbing shrub. Leaves entire, cordate, obtuse, largely petiolate, up to 12 cm long. Hermaphrodite flowers, solitary, axillar, pendulouos from long peduncles. Perianth made up of a doubled, oblong-ovoid tube opening into a limb obcordiform-ovate, with purple spots on yellowish background, up to 50 cm long and about 40 cm wide. Fruit capsular.
Not particular about soil. It prefers a sunny location. Fast growing. Used in gardening to cover walls, pergolas, etc.

Flowering: Almost year-round.
Propagation: By seeds, cuttings and air layering.

Bougainvilla X buttiana Holtt. et Stand. **_'Mrs. Butt'_** Nyctaginaceae.

BOUGAINVILLEA

A woody climbing plant, evergreen and spiny. Leaves alternate, broadly ovate, acuminate, glabrous, paler beneath than above, up to 20 cm long. Flowers hermaphrodite in clusters of three, each subtended by a scarlet bract; obtuse, apiculate, undulated. Calyx tubular, pubescent, five-lobed, star-shaped, acting as the corolla since it is absent. Up to 1 cm long. Fruit in achene.

It accepts most soils and needs a sunny location. Resistant to drought. Fast growing.

Used in gardening to cover pergolas, walls, taluses, etc.

Flowering: Nearly year-round.
Propagation: By cuttings.

Bougainvillea glabra Choisy. 'Sanderiana'. Nyctaginaceae.

PAPER FLOWER

A woody climbing plant, evergreen, inermous or with curved thorns. Leaves alternate, narrowly ovate to elliptical, acuminate, glabrous or slightly puberulent, paler beneath than above, up to 11 cm long. Flowers hermaphrodite, in clusters of three, each subtended by a purple bract, with the apex acute, undulated. Has a tubular pubescent calyx, with five lobes forming a star, acting as the corolla since it is absent; purple in colour, up to 1 cm long. Fruit in achene.

It accepts most soils and requires a sunny situation. Resistant to drought. Fast growing.

Used in gardening to cover pergolas, walls, etc.

Flowering: Nearly year-round.
Propagation: By cuttings.

Bougainvillea spectabilis Willd. Nyctaginaceae. Brazil.

BOUGAINVILLEA

A woody climber, evergreen, spiny with pubescent branches. Leaves alternate, ovate, tomentose beneath and very often also above. Up to 12 cm long. Flowers hermaphrodite in clusters of three, each subtended by a purple bract, up to 4.5 cm long. Has a tubular calyx with five lobes forming a star, acting as a corolla since it is absent, up to 2.2 cm long with abundant hair up to 1 mm long or more. Fruit in achene.

Not particular regarding soil. It requires location in bright sun. Drought resistant. Fast growing.

Used in gardening to cover walls, pergolas, taluses, etc.

Flowering: Winter-spring-early summer.
Propagation: By cuttings.

Bougainvillea spectablls Willd. **_Cv. Lateritia._** Nyctaginaceae.

BOUGAINVII I FA

A woody climber, evergreen, spiny, with pubescent branches. Leaves alternate, ovate, tomentose beneath and very often also above. Up to 12 cm long. Flowers hermaphrodite in clusters of three, each subtended by a brick red bract up to 5.5 cm long. Has a tutular calyx, star-shaped, five lobed, acting as a corolla since it is absent, up to 2.5 cm long, with abundant hair up to 1 mm long or more. Fruit in achene.

Not particular as far as soil. It needs to be located in bright sun. Resistant to little water. Fast growing.

Used in gardening to cover pergolas, walls, taluses, etc.

Flowering: Autumn-winter-spring-early summer.
Propagation: By cuttings.

Brachychilum horsfieldii (R. Br.) Petersen. Zingiberaceae. Java.

A perennial herbaceous plant, rhizomatous, up to 80 cm high. Leaves entire, lanceolate or linear-lanceolate, paler beneath, up to 30 cm long or more and 8.5 cm broad. Flowers hermaphrodite clustered on a sparsely dense terminal spike. Tubular calyx. The tube of the corolla is long, slender, yellowish, with twisted linear lobes. Very short staminoid lip, bipartite, white. Two lateral staminodes, similar to petals, also white, up to 2 cm long. Fruits in capsules, with orange inside, containing dark seeds with red arils.

Prefers rich soils, abundant moisture and a partially shaded spot. Dry stems must be pruned at ground level to favour new shoots. Fast growing.

Used in gardening to form groups.

Flowering: Summer-autumn-winter.
Propagation: By seed and division.

Brahea armata S. Wats. [*Erythea armata* (S. Wats.) S. Wats.].
Palmae. Baja California.

BLUE FAN PALM

Hermaphroditic Palm, thick trunk, up to 12 m high or more. Leaves palmate, blue, up to 2.60 m long, deeply divided in about 60 segments bipartite, slightly filiferous. Petioles with spiny margins. Inflorescence longer than leaves, about 4.5 m long or more, branched, with branches pendulous. Flowers in clusters of three. Fruit globose, flat on one side, about 2.5 cm long, yellow.

Accepts most soils. Needs sunny location. Very slow growing. Dry leaves persist on trunk for some time.

In gardening, used individually or in groups.

Propagation: By seeds.

Brassaia actinophylla Endl. [*Schefflera actynophylla* (Endl.) Harms.]. Araliaceae. Australia.

AUSTRALIAN UMBRELLA TREE

Evergreen tree up to 12 m high, often presenting several trunks. Leaves composite, digitate. Petioles up to 75 cm long. Folioles oblong, glossy, up to 60 cm long, growing from apex of petiole. Small flowers, red, grouped in umbels arranged in racemes up to 1 cm long. Fruit in drupe, red-purple in colour.

Prefers good quality soils. Needs sunny location, although it accepts partial shade. Fast growing.

In gardening used individually or in groups. Also as potted plant for interior decoration and patios.

Flowering: End summer-autumn.
Reproduction: By seed, cutting, shoot and air layering.

Breynia disticha J. R. Forst. et G. Forst. [*B. nivosa* (W. G. Sm.) Small]. Euphorbiaceae. Pacific Islands.

SNOWBUSH

Shrub monoecious, evergreen, up to 2 m high. Leaves alternate, simple, entire, elliptical to ovate or obovate, slightly distichous, up to 5 cm long, green and white. Flowers unisexual, small, dull. Females bell-shaped, reddish. Fruits in berries.

Cv. Roseo-Picta. Leaves with green, white, pink and red.

Not demanding about soil. Accepts shade, but in strong sun it takes on more attractive colouring. Somewhat slow growing.

Used in gardening individually, in groups and for hedges. Also as potted plant.

Propagation: By cuttings and shoots.

Brugmansia X candida Pers. [*Datura X candida* (Pers.) Saff.; *B. aurea X B.* versicolor]. Solanaceae. Ecuador.

ANGEL'S-TRUMPET

Evergreen shrub or small tree up to 6 m high. Leaves alternate, ovate to oblong-elliptical, acuminate, entire to coarsely dentate, slightly pubescent, up to 55 cm long, largely petiolate. Flowers large, pendulous, white, rarely yellow or pink. Calyx spathe-looking, up to 12 cm long, with only one tooth ending in prolonged tip. Corolla funnel-shaped, 5-toothed, up to 27 cm long. Teeth curved, long. Fruits in berries oblong-cilindric to fusiform, up to 18 cm long.

Not demanding about soil. Can live both in sun and shade. Needs appropriate fertilizing and watering for good growth. Needs pruning to have better shape. Fast growing.

All parts of the plant are poisonous if eaten in large quantity. In small dosis they produce narcotic effects due to presence of alkaloids.

Used in gardening individually or in groups.

Flowering: Almost year-round.
Propagation: By seed and cutting.

Brugmansia X insignis (Barb. Rodr.) Lockw.: *B. suaveolens X* B. versicolor. Solanaceae. Peruvian Andes.

ANGEL'S-TRUMPET

Shrub or small tree, evergreen up to 4.5 m high. Leaves alternate, ovate or narrowly elliptical, acute to acuminate, entire or sinuate, pubescent up to 30 cm long, largely petiolate. Flowers hermaphrodite, semipendulous. Corolla white, up to 28 cm long. 5-toothed, with curved teeth, longer than those of *B. suaveolens*. Anthers connivent or not. Fruits in berries, fusiform.

Little demanding about soil. Can live in strong sun as well as in shade. Needs appropriate fertilizer and watering for good growth. Must be pruned to give it shape. Fast growing.

Contains alkaloids with strong narcotic effects, thus consumption of any part of the plant, in some amount, has mortal consequences.

Used in gardening to form groups or individually.

Flowering: Autumn to spring.
Reproduction: By seed and cutting.

Brugmansia sanguinea (Ruiz et Pavón). D. Don. [*Datura sanguinea* Ruiz et Pavón]. Solanaceae. The Andes, from Colombia to Chile.

ANGEL'S-TRUMPET

Shrub or small tree, evergreen, normally up to 3.5 m high, with young branches pubescent. Leaves alternate, ovate-oblong, coarsely dentate, pubescent, with beneath paler than above, acute, up to 25 cm long. Petioles long, pubescent. Flowers hermaphrodite, pendulous, funnel-shaped. Calyx with 1-4 teeth. Corolla red in colour with some yellow at the mouth, then changing to yellow and yellowish-green towards the base of the tube, up to 18 cm long, with five curved teeth. Fruits in berries.

Accepts most soils. Tolerates completely sunny location and also shade. Needs good fertilizing and watering for good growth. Needs pruning into shape. Fast growing.

The presence of alkaloids makes all parts of the plant poisonous if eaten in large quantity. In small dosis they have narcotic effects.

Used in gardening as sole individual or in groups.

Flowering: Nearly year-round.
Propagation: By seed and cutting.

Brugmansia suaveolens (Humb. et Bonpl. ex Willd.) Bercht. et J. Presl. [*Datura suaveolens* Humb. et Bonpl. ex Willd.]. Solanaceae. Brazil.

ANGEL'S-TRUMPET

Shrub or small tree, evergreen, up to 4.5 m high. Leaves alternate, ovate to narrowly elliptical, acute, entire, glabrous, up to 23 cm long. Flowers hermaphrodite, semipendulous, funnel-shaped to campanulate. Calyx with 2-5 teeth. Corolla white, 5-toothed, with non-curved teeth, up to 23 cm long. Anthers connivent. Fruits in berries, fusiform, up to 15 cm long.

Tolerates most soils. Thrives in strong sun or shade. Needs appropriate fertilizing and watering for good growth. Must be pruned to be shaped. Fast growing.

As it contains alkaloids, all parts of the plant are poisonous if eaten in large quantity. In small amounts they have narcotic effects.

Used in gardening individually or in groups.

Flowering: Late spring-summer.
Propagation: By seed and cutting.

Brugmansia versicolor Lagerth. [*Datura mollis* Saff.]. Solanaceae.
Ecuador.

ANGEL'S-TRUMPET

Evergreen small tree up to 4.5 m high. Leaves alternate, oblong-elliptical, glabrous to pubescent, acuminate, largely petiolate, up to 60 cm long. Flowers hemaphrodite, large, pendulous, funnel-shaped. Spathe-like calyx, up to 17 cm long, with one sole tooth ending in a long tip. Corolla 5-toothed, funnel-shaped, with teeth long and curved, at its beginning it is white with light salmon tints becoming peach-coloured, up to 30 cm long. Fruits in berries, fusiform, up to 21 cm long.

Tolerates most soils. Lives in strong sun as well as in shade. Needs appropriate fertilizing and watering for good growth. Must be pruned into shape. Fast growing.

All parts of the plant are poisonous if eaten in large quantities; however, in small dosis they have narcotic effects due to their alkaloid contents.

Used in gardening individually or in groups.

Flowering: Almost all year.
Propagation: By seed and cutting.

Calliandra haematocephala Hassk. Leguminosae. Bolivia.

Shrub or small tree, evergreen up to 4.5 m high or more. Leaves alternate, bipinnate, with two pinnas. Folioles obliquely oblong-lanceolate up to 4 cm long. Flowers hermaphrodite or functionally male in globose heads up to 7 cm in diameter. Corolla reddish. Stamen very long, with red filaments. Fruits in legumes, linear-oblanceolate.

Accepts most soils although prefers rich, well drained ones. Needs sunny location. Moderate growth.

Used in gardening individually or in groups.

Flowering: Autumn-winter-spring.
Propagation: By seed and cutting.

Carissa macrocarpa (Eckl.) A. DC. [*C. grandiflora* (E. H. Mey). A. DC.]. Apocynaceae. South Africa.

NATAL PLUM

Evergreen shrub, up to 4 m high, very ramified, spiny. Leaves opposite, broadly ovate, coriaceous, mucronate, dark green above and paler underneath, up to 10 cm long. Flowers hermaphrodite, clustered in terminal cymes with few flowers, sometimes one sole flower. Corolla salverform, up to 6 cm in diameter, white, fragant, with tube up to 1.5 cm long and lobes oblong to elliptical much longer than tube. Fruits in berries, ovoid scarlet coloured up to 5 cm long.

Prefers light, well-drained soils. Grows better in dry, sunny places. Resistent to sea mist. Slow growing.
Fruit edible fresh or used in preparing preserves and jams.
In gardening used individually to form groups and hedges. Recommended for coastal gardens.

Flowering: Nearly year-round.
Propagation: By seed, cuttings and air layering.

37

Caryota mitis [*C. furfuracea* Blume]. Palmae. Burma to Malaccan Peninsula, Java and Philippines.

BURMESE FISHTAIL PALM

Palm monoecious that usually produces several trunks, up to 3.5 m high and about 15 cm in diameter. Leaves bipinnate about 2.5 m long, with pinnules obliquely cuneate, dentate, similar to a fish tail. Inflorescences branched, with sprigs pendulous, having unisexual flowers. The inflorescences appear first in the upper part of trunk and then gradually lower until the fruit of the lowest one ripens; then the trunk dies. Fruit globose, reddish, up to 1.5 cm in diameter.

Needs rich soil and abundant moisture. Prefers a sunny location, accepting some shade. Fast growing. In gardening used individually or in groups. Also as a potted plant for decorating patios.

Propagation: By seed.

Cibotium schiedei Schlechtend. et Cham. Dicksoniaceae. Mexico and Guatemala.

MEXICAN TREE FERN

Tree fern up to 4.5 m high that sometimes produces sprouts at its base. Trunk and bases of the petioles covered with silky hairs yellow-brown in colour. Fronds tripinnate, oblong-deltoid, glacous beneath, graciously arched, up to nearly 3 m long. Primary divisions oblong-lanceolate, up to 70 cm long. Secundary pinnas linear-lanceolate. Pinnules lanceolate, serrate. Sorus with bivalve indusium, valves similar in texture, but different from that of the fronds.

Needs soil rich in organic material, with good drainage. Also needs shady location. Slow growing.

Long hairs covering the cauline apex have been used as a bandage like cotton.

In gardening used as individual sample or in groups. Also as potted plant.

Propagation: By spores.

Clerodendrum speciosissimum Van Geert. [*C. fallax* Lindl.].
Verbenaceae. Java.

PAGODA FLOWER

Evergreen shrub up to 3.5 m high. Branches tetragonal. Leaves opposite, cordate-ovate, thickly pubescent, entire or dentate, up to 27 cm long. Petioles long, pubescent. Flowers hermaphrodite, scarlet, up to 3.5 cm in diameter, in cymes forming panicles terminal erect up to 40 cm long. Tube of corolla up to 1.5 cm long. Stamens exserted and curved. Fruits in drupes, bluish-black in colour, with two grooves perpendicular subtended by the reddish calyx.

Accepts most soils. Needs exposure to strong sun or half shade, and plenty of water. Pruning best after flowering to prevent leggyness.

Widely used in gardening for its beautiful flowering, individually as well as in groups.

Flowering: Nearly year-round.
Propagation: By seed and cuttings.

Clivia X cyrtanthiflora (vab Houtte) Wittm.: C. miniata X C. nobilis.
Amaryllidaceae.

Plant herbaceous, perennial, acaulescent, with carnose roots.
Leaves perennial, obtuse, strap-shaped canaliculate, glossy.
surpassing 90 cm long and up to 5.5 cm wide. Flowers
hermaphrodite, pendulous, grouped in umbels. Perianth petaloid,
curved, funnel-shaped, up to 4.5 cm long and 3.2 cm in diameter,
with short tube and lobes with reddish and yellowish tones. Fruits in
berries.
Prefers rich soils, with good drainage and plenty of moisture.
Needs a shady location.
Used in gardening to form groups. Also as potted plant.

Flowering: Nearly year-round.
Propagation: By seed and division.

Clivia miniata Regel. Amaryllidaceae. South Africa.

KAFFIR LILY

Plant herbaceous, perennial, acaulescent, with fleshy roots. Leaves perennial, arched, strap-shaped, up to 65 cm long and almost 4 cm wide, glossy, ending in point. Flowers erect, hermaphrodite, clustered in umbels. Perianth petaloid, funnel-shaped, up to 7.5 cm long, with very short tube and lobes reddish with yellowish base. Fruits in berries, ovoid, red in colour.

Prefers rich soils, with good drainage and abundant moisture. Needs shady site.

In gardening used to form groups. Also as potted plant for decorating patios and interiors.

Flowering: Spring-early summer.
Propagation: By seed and division.

Colletia cruciata Hook. Rhamnaceae. South of Brazil and Uruguay.

ANCHOR PLANT

Deciduous shrub up to 3 m high. Branches with triangular thorns up to 5 cm long, flat which are actually modified sprigs ending in very sharp point. Each pair of thorns is arranged in a right angle to the pairs immediately before and after it. Leaves ovate, small, usually absent. Flowers hermaphrodite, small, yellowish-white, apetalous, tubular, solitary or forming groups at the base of the thorns. Fruit capsuled.

Little demanding regarding soil, as long as it is well drained. Needs a sunny location. Slow growing. Drought resistant.

Used in gardening alone or in groups.

Flowering: Nearly year-round.
Propagation: By seed and cuttings.

Crinum moorei Hook. f. Amaryllidaceae. South Africa.

MOORE'S CRINUM

Plant herbaceous, perennial, with thick tunicate bulbs, having a long neck up to 65 cm long. Leaves ensiform, canaliculate, entire, arched, up to 125 cm long and 15 cm wide. Flowers hermaphrodite, clustered in umbel at end of floral scape up to 150 cm long. Perianth petaloid, funnel-shaped, up to 20 cm in diameter or more, with tepals oblong, acute, white with rosaceous tones. Curved tube up to 12 cm long, green. Fruit capsuled.

Needs rich soil with good drainage and plenty of moisture. Can live in strong sun as well as in shade, although it prefers partial shade.

Used in gardening in groups. Also in large flower pots.

Flowering: Spring-summer.
Propagation: By seed and division.

Crinum pedunculatum R. Br. Amaryllidaceae. Australia.

Plant herbaceous, perennial, with tunicate bulbs, having a thick neck up to 45 cm long. Leaves perennial, ensiform, canaliculate, up to 160 cm long and 14 cm wide. Flowers hermaphrodite, clustered in umbel at the end of a floral scape up to 120 cm long. Perianth petaloid, salverform, up to 17 cm in diameter with tepals linear, white in colour. Tube straight or somewhat curved up to 8 cm long, green. Fruit capsuled.

Needs rich soil with abundant moisture and good drainage. Prefers strong sun or partial shade.

Used in gardening in groups. Also in large flower pots.

Flowering: Spring-summer.
Reproduction: By seed and division.

Cryptostegia madagascariensis Bojer. Asclepiadaceae.
Madagascar.

PURPLE ALAMANDA

Plant woody climber, evergreen. Leaves simple, opposite, somewhat revolute, glabrous, oblong, acuminate, dark green in colour and glossy above and paler beneath, up to 10 cm long. Hermaphrodite flowers grouped in cymes terminal. Corolla funnel-shaped, five-lobed, purple, up to 5.5 cm in diameter. Crown with entire lobes. Fruits in follicles, in pairs, greenish, up to 10 cm long.

Accepts most soils. Needs a sunny site. After pruning it has a shrubbish appearance. Somewhat slow growing.

Used in gardening to cover pergolas, walls, etc.

Flowering: Late spring-summer-autumn.
Propagation: By seed and cuttings.

Cuphea ignea A. DC. [*C. platycentra* Lem., not Benth.]. Lythraceae. Mexico and Jamaica.

CIGAR FLOWER

Perennifoliate shrub up to 90 cm high. Leaves opposite, oblong to lanceolate, up to 4 cm long or more. Flowers hermaphrodite, tubulose, apetalous, axillary. Calyx up to 2.5 cm long, with scarlet-coloured tube and violet limb with white segment. Fruits in capsules.

Not demanding regarding soil. Thrives in strong sun as well as in shade. Needs plenty of water. Slow growing.

Flowers look like small lit cigars.

Used in gardening individually or in groups.

Flowering: Nearly year-round.
Propagation: By seed and cuttings.

Dichrostachys cinerea (L.) Wight et Arn. **subsp. cinerea.**
Leguminosae. Arabia, Egypt to Zimbabwe.

AROMA

Shrub to small tree with caducous leaves, spiny, with parasol-shaped top. Leaves alternate, bipinnate, up to 11 cm long. Folioles linear, up to 2 mm wide and 6 mm long. Flowers in spikes pendulous with long petioles. Flowers of the basal part are sterile, with long staminodes pink or white. Apex flowers are hermaphrodite, yellow. Fruits in legumes, flat, undulated and twisted.

Not demanding as far as soil. Needs sunny site. Drought resistant.

Leaves and fruit are used to feed livestock. Roots and leaves are used in popular medicine for snake and scorpion bites.

Used as ornament in parks and gardens.

Flowering: Autumn.
Reproduction: By seed.

Dictyosperma album (Bory) H. Wendl. et Drude ex Scheff. [*D. rubrum* Nichols.]. Palmae. Mascarene Islands.

PRINCESS PALM

Palm monoecious with grayish trunk, annulate, up to 14 m high or more. Leaves pinnate up to 3.60 m long. Shells of leaves form a crownshaft. Pinnas linear-lanceolate, acuminate, up to 60 cm long, with veins well marked. Inflorescence in lower part of culm, up to 40 cm long. Flowers in triads, two male and one female. Fruit ellipsoidal, up to 2 cm long, purple.

Prefers rich, well-drained soils. Needs sunny location. Fast growing.

In gardening used individually or in groups. Also as potted plant for interior decoration.

Propagation: By seed.

50

Distictis buccinatoria (DC.) A. Gentry [_Phaedranthus buccinatorius_ (DC.) Miers]. Bignoniaceae. Mexico.

> BLOOD-TRUMPET

Woody climbing plant, evergreen. Quadrangular branches. Leaves opposite made up of two folioles and a terminal tendril. Folioles elliptical to obovate-oblong, acuminate, up to 11 cm long. Flowers hermaphrodite clustered in terminal racemes pendulous, with few flowers. Corolla tubular funnel-shaped, up to 8 cm long, pentalobed, with yellowish tubes with reddish tones and the limb blood red or purple-red. Stamens exserted. Fruits in capsules.

Not particular about soil, as long as well-drained. Needs sunny site. Fast growing. Prefers abundant watering.

Used to cover walls, pergolas, etc.

Flowering: Nearly all year.
Propagation: Usually, by cuttings and air layering.

Duranta repens. L. [*D. plumieri* Jacq.]. Verbenaceae. Florida to
Brazil.

GOLDEN-DEWDROP

Shrub or small tree up to 5.5 m high, occasionally spiny, with branches graciously arched. Leaves simple, opposite or verticillate, ovate to obovate, entire or coarsely dentate in upper part, up to 13.5 cm long. Flowers hermaphrodite, grouped in panicles. Corolla salverform, pentalobed, lilac in colour, up to 12 mm in diameter. Fruits in drupes, yellow, approx. 1 cm in diameter.

Accepts most soils. Resists drought, but grows better with plenty of water. Prefers sunny location, although allows partial shade. Fast growing. Should be pruned after fruit falls in order to obtain better flowering.

Used in gardening individually, in groups or as hedge.

Flowering: Nearly year-round.
Propagation: By seed and cuttings.

Erythrina caffra Thunb. Leguminosae. South Africa.

ERYTHRINA, COAST KAFFIRBOOM

Deciduous tree up to 20 m high, with trunk branches spiny. Leaves alternate, imparipinnate, largely petiolate. Folioles in threes (sometimes fives), rhomboidal-ovate, acuminate, the central one larger than side ones, up to 16 cm wide. Flowers hermaphrodite, red-orange in colour (sometimes cream-coloured), clustered on racemes. Standard strongly reflex, up to 6 cm long and 4 cm wide, not enclosing other parts of the flower. Fruits in legumes, constricting, curved, up to 20 cm long. Seeds red, glossy, with dark-coloured hilum.

Tolerates most soils. Prefers sunny location. Resistant to droughts and frost. Fast growing.

The flowering of this tree, which begins when leafless, indicates to the Bantus that it is time to sow their crops. The seeds, poisonous, are used by the native women to make necklaces as they are thought to bring good luck. The wood is used to make canoes.

In gardening it is used as a shade tree in parks and gardens and urban alignments.

Flowering: Winter-early spring.
Propagation: By seed and cuttings.

Ficus auriculata Lour. [*F. roxburghii* Wallich ex Miq.]. Moraceae.
Himalaya.

HIMALAYAN FIG TREE

Deciduous shrub or tree up to 6 m high. Leaves broadly ovate or
rounded. Petioles long, up to 25 cm long or more. Limbs acute
or acuminate, cordate base, up to 45 cm long. Fruit pear-shaped or
somewhat globose, yellowish or reddish, up to 6 cm in diameter
or more, appearing on branches and trunk.

Tolerates most soils. Prefers a sunny site, although resists shade.
Slow growing.

Very ornamental, used in parks and gardens.

Propagation: By air layering and cuttings.

Ficus pumila L. [_F. stipulata_ Thunb.; _F. repens_ Hort., not Willd.].
Moraceae. Eastern Asia.

CREEPING FIG

Evergreen climber. Branches with fruit erect, with leaves elliptical or oblong, entire, with margins revolute, glossy green above and paler beneath, up to 10 cm long. Fruitless branches with roots adventitious, that it uses to fix itself and climb, and leaves sessile or shortly petiolate, cordate-ovate, up to 6 cm long and 4 cm in diameter.

Allows most soils. Can live in strong sun as well as in shade. Slow growing.

Used in gardening to cover walls, pergolas, etc.

Propagation: By cuttings and air layering.

Gardenia cornuta Hemsl. Rubiaceae. South Africa.

Evergreen shrub or small tree, up to 4.5 m high, with branches erect and twigs sometimes spiny. Leaves opposite or verticillate, obovate to oblanceolate, up to 12.5 cm long. Flowers hermaphrodite, solitary, fragrant, appearing at the end of sprigs. Calyx tubular, with six cylindrical appendages. Corolla salverform, up to 6.5 cm in diameter, with tube greenish-white up to 7.5 cm long and white lobes. Fruits in berries, oval or pyriform, golden and up to 5 cm long.

Prefers soils rich in organic matter and an adequate water supplement. Needs a sunny or partially sunny location. Somewhat resistant to cold and drought. Slow growing.

The Zulus prepare an infusion with the fruit and roots which they use as an emetic. The wood is used for fences and firewood.

In gardening it is used individually or in groups.

Flowering: Summer.
Propagation: By seed and cutting.

Garenia thunbergia L. F. Rubiaceae. South Africa.

Evergreen shrub up to 3 m high. Leaves opposite or verticillate, elliptical, up to 18 cm long. Flowers hermaphrodite, solitary, fragrant, appearing at the end of the sprigs. Calyx tubular, with a terminal cleft, with appendages foliaceous. Corolla salverform, up to 7.5 cm in diameter, with tube greenish-white, up to 6 cm long and limb formed by eight white overlapping lobes. Fruits in berries, ovoid, woody, grayish, up to 5 cm long or more.

Prefers good quality soils and regular watering. Indicated for bright sun or partial shade. Somewhat resistant to cold and drought. Slow growing.

The roots are used for treating skin eruptions and as an emetic. The wood for making tools, etc.

In gardening used individually or in groups.

Flowering: Summer.
Propagation: By seed and cuttings.

Goethea strictiflora Hook. Malvaceae. Brazil.

Evergreen shrub up to 2 m high. Leaves alternate, ovate to ovate-elliptical, coriaceous, sinuate-dentate, up to 30 cm long or more. Flowers hermaphrodite clustered in cymes, appearing on very short sprigs along the stem. Flowers are protected by four bracts (calyculus) ocordate to triangular or ovate, reddish, up to 2 cm long. Calyx pentalobed. Corolla more or less tubular. Fruit in schizocarp.

Not particular regarding soil. Prefers sunny location, although it accepts some shade.

In gardening used individually or to form groups.

Flowering: Nearly year-round.
Propagation: Usually by cuttings.

Haemanthus puniceus L. Amaryllidaceae. South Africa.

Plant bulbous with leaves oblong, slender, undulated, acute, spotted with purple in the basal part, up to 55 cm long and 14 cm wide. Flowers hermaphrodite clustered in umbellate capitulum up to 12 cm in diameter appearing at the end of a scape pale green in colour with purple dots at the base, thick, carnose, up to 55 cm long or more. Bracts tinted purple. Perianth corolline, light scarlet to white, up to 3 cm long, with tube shorter than the narrow, erect segments. Stamens exserted, with yellow anthers. Fruits in berries.

Prefers rich, well drained soils. Grows better in a shady site, although it accepts bright sun.

Used in gardening to form groups. Also as potted plant.

Flowering: Winter.
Propagation: By seed and division.

Hedychium coronarium J. König. Zingiberaceae. Tropical Asia.

WHITE GINGER

Plant herbaceous, perennial, rhizomatous, up to 1.80 m high, with many stems. Leaves alternate, distichous, oblong-lanceolate to lanceolate, sheathing, hairy underneath, up to 60 cm long. Flowers hermaphrodite, white, fragant, clustered in spikes. Tube of corolla slender, up to 8.5 cm long. Lobes of corolla narrow. Staminode lip large, approx. 5 cm long, bilobed, sometimes with yellow spot on base. Staminodes lateral similar to petals. Fruits in capsules.

Needs rich soil and abundant moisture. Prefers partially shady site. Fast growing.

Used in gardening to form groups. Also as potted plant.

Flowering: Late summer-autumn.
Propagation: By seed and division.

Hedychium gardnerianum Roscoe. Zingiberaceae. India

KAHILI GINGER

Plant herbaceous, perennial, rhizomatous, up to 1.80 m high or more. Leaves alternate, distichous, sheathing, glabrous, lanceolate or oblong-lanceolate glaucous beneath, up to 40 cm long. Flowers hermaphrodite, yellow, fragrant, clustered in spikes up to 30 cm long or more. Tube of corolla up to 5.5 cm long, with lobes linear, involute and recurved. Staminode lip bilobed, up to 3 cm long. Filament of stamen red, exserted. Fruits in capsules.

Required rich soil and abundant moisture. Prefers partially sunny site. Fast growing. More rustic than the rest of the hedychium species grown.

Used in gardening to form groups. Also as potted plant.

Flowering: Summer-autumn.
Reproduction: By seed and division.

Heliconia bihai (L.) L. [*H. humilis* Jacq.; *H. caribaea* auct. non Lam.].
Musaceae. West Indies and northern South America.

WILD PLANTAIN

Plant herbaceous, rhizomatous, with habit of growing musroid, up to 5 m high. Leaves distichous, oblong, acuminate. Petioles usually glabrous, up to 110 cm long. Limbs up to 100 cm long or more. Inflorescence erect up to 65 cm long. Spathes distichous to irregularly arranged, not reflexed at the end, up to 30 cm long, glabrous to somewhat hairy, boat-shaped, red on sides, yellow in the carina and margins yellow and/or green. Spathes not overlapping or only at the base, containing several greenish flowers clustered in cincinnus. Fruits in capsules.

Prefers rich soils and abundant moisture. Better in a sunny or partially sunny site. Fast growing.

In gardening used to form groups. Also grown for cut flowers.

Flowering: Summer-autumn.
Propagation: By seed and division.

Hymenocallis littoralis (Jacq.) Salisb. Amaryllidaceae. Tropical America.

SPIDER LILY

Plant herbaceous, bulbous, acaulescent, losing its leaves in winter. These are basal, strap-shaped, canaliculate, up to 1 m long and approx. 4 cm wide. Flowers hermaphrodite, white, fragrant, arranged in umbel at the end of a floral scape longer than the leaves. Perianth salverform. Tube up to 16 cm long or more. Lobes linear, up to 11 cm long or more, curved. Crown funnel-shaped joining base of the six stamen. Free part of filaments up to 7 cm long. Style longer than stamens.

Not particular regarding soil. Prefers partially shady site. Resists being near the sea.

In gardening used to form groups. Also as potted plant.

Flowering: Summer-autumn.
Propagation: By seed and division.

Ipomoea acuminata (Vahl) Roem. et Schult. [*I. learii* Paxt.]
Convolvulaceae. Tropical America.

BLUE DAWN FLOWER

Climber evergreen. Leaves broadly ovate to orbicular, ocordate, entire or three-lobed, pubescent underneath, up to 15 cm long. Flowers hermaphrodite clustered in racemes. Calyx pubescent, with sepals acuminate. Corolla funnel-shaped, pink-purple in colour, up to 8 cm long and same in diameter, with 10 strias. Fruits in capsules.
Not particular about soil. Requires sunny location. Fast growing.
Used in gardening to cover walls, fences, pergolas, etc.

Flowering: Nearly all year.
Propagation: By seed and cuttings.

Ipomoea horsfalliae Hook. Convolvulaceae. West Indies.

Climber woody, evergreen. Leaves palmatilobed to palmatisect, with 5-7 lobes, thick, glabrous, up to 16.5 cm long. Flowers hermaphrodite, clustered in cymes dichotomous. Corolla campanulate, pink or purple, up to 4 cm long and 4 cm in diameter. Fruits in capsules.

Accepts most soils. Prefers sunny location. Tolerates being near the sea.

In gardening used to cover pergolas, walls, etc.

Flowering: Autumn-winter.
Propagation: By seed, cuttings, air layering and grafting.

Iresine herbstii Hook. [*I. reticulata* Hort.; *Achyranthos herbstii* Hort.].
Amaranthaceae. South America.

BEEF PLANT

Herb perennial, up to 1.80 m high, with stem and branches reddish. Leaves opposite, broadly ovate to orbicular, obtuse, emarginated, red-purple, with nervations lighter coloured. Limbs up to 9.5 cm long. Petioles up to 8 cm long. Flowers small, whitish, clustered in spikes arranged in panicles. Fruit in utricle, indehiscent.

Prefers rich, well drained soils and abundant water. Needs sunny site. Accepts trimming. Fast growing.

Used in gardening to form masses of colour and for hedges.

Propagation: By cuttings.

Iresine herbstii Hook. **Cv. Aureo-reticulata.** Amaranthaceae.

Herb perennial, up to 1.80 m high, with stem and branches reddish. Leaves opposite, broadly ovate, acute to acuminate, green with yellowish nervations. Limbs up to 17 cm long. Petioles reddish, up to 6 cm long. Flowers small, whitish, clustered in spikes arranged in panicles. Fruit in utricle, indehiscent.

Prefers rich, well drained soils and abundant moisture. Requires sunny situation. Fast growing. Accepts trimming.

Used in gardening to form masses of colour and for hedges.

Propagation: By cuttings.

Jasminum azoricum L. Oleaceae. Madeira.

Climbing shrub evergreen. Leaves opposite, trifoliolate, with folioles ovate, acute to acuminate, undulated, glossy green above and lighter beneath. Side folioles shortly petiolate, smaller than the terminal, reaching 10 cm in length. Flowers hermaphrodite, fragrant, clustered in cymes axillary and terminal. Corolla salverform up to 2.5 cm in diameter, white with purple tints in the tube and outer part of lobes, which are more or less lanceolate. Fruits in berries.

Accepts most soils. Prefers sunny location. Somewhat slow growing. Used in gardening to cover walls, pergolas, etc.

Flowering: Nearly year-round.
Propagation: Usually by cuttings.

Jasminum mesnyi Hance [*J. primulinum* Hemsl.]. Oleaceae. China.

JAPANESE JASMINE

Shrub evergreen up to 3 m high, with branches quadrangular. Leaves opposite, trifoliolate, with spiny margins, dark green above and lighter beneath. Side folioles sessile, smaller than terminal, reaching 11 cm in length. Flowers hermaphrodite, solitary, in axils of leaves, often double, 3-4.5 cm in diameter. Corolla yellow, salverform, with orange strias in narrow part. Short tube.

Not particular regarding soil. Prefers sunny location. Somewhat resistant to frost.

Used in gardening to cover walls.

Flowering: Winter-spring.
Reproduction: Normally by cuttings.

Jasminum polyanthum Franch. Oleaceae. China.

CHINESE JASMINE

Deciduous shrub, sometimes evergreen, usually climber. Leaves opposite, pinnate, with 5-7 folioles lanceolate, trinerviate from base, lighter beneath. Bases of petioles broad, almost winged, more or less amplexicaul. Side folioles shorter than terminal, reaching 8 cm in length. Flowers hermaphrodite, fragrant, up to 3 cm in diameter, clustered in axillary panicles. Calyx pentalobed, with lobes subulate, not exceeding 2 mm long. Corolla white, salverform, with rosaceous tints on tube and outer part of lobes. Tube 20-22 mm long. Lobes 4-5. Fruits in berries.

Prefers rich, well drained soils and a sunny location. Fast growing. Shows some resistance to frost.

Used in gardening to cover pergolas, walls, etc.

Flowering: Winter-spring.
Reproduction: By seed and cuttings.

Justicia aurea Schlechtend. [*J. umbrosa* Benth.; *Jacobinia aurea* (Schlechtend.) Hemsl., not Hiern]. Acanthaceae. Mexico and Central America.

Shrub evergreen up to 3.5 m high, with stems and branches obtusely quadrangular. Leaves opposite, ovate or lanceolate-oblong, with prominent veins beneath, up to 40 cm long, decurrent, acuminate. Petioles up to 8 cm long. Flowers hermaphrodite, in dense terminal spikes, up to 18 cm long. Bracts and sepals linear-lanceolate, tinted purple. Corolla yellow, tubular, bilabiate, curved, open almost half-way, up to 8 cm long. Fruits in capsules.

Prefers rich, well drained soils. Requires abundant water. Although accepts bright sun, better in partially shady spots. Fast growing. Pruning convenient after flowering.

Used in gardening to form groups or individually.

Flowering: End of autumn-winter.
Reproduction: Normally by cuttings.

Justicia rizzinii Wassh. [_J. floribunda_ Hort.; _J. pauciflora_ (Nees) Griseb., non Vahl; _Jacobina pauciflora_ (Nees) Lindau]. Acanthaceae. Brazil.

Shrub evergreen up to 60 cm high. Branches pubescent. Leaves opposite, entire, elliptical o elliptical-oblong, acute to acuminate, up to 3.5 m long. Each pair of leaves are slightly unequal in size. Petioles short. Flowers hermaphrodite, clustered in axillary spikes with few flowers, semipendulous or pendulous. Corolla tubular, angulous, bilabiate, with basal part red and apical yellow, up to 2.5 cm long. Fruits in capsules.

Prefers rich, well drained soils. Although accepts bright sun, grows better in partially shady sites. Slow growing.

Used in gardening as solitary plant or to form groups. Also as potted plant.

Flowering: Late autumn-winter-spring.
Propagation: By seed and cuttings.

Leucospermum cordifolium (Salisb. ex Knight) Fourcade [*L. Nutans* R. BR.]. Proteaceae. South Africa.

NODDING PINCUSHION

Shrub evergreen up to 1.5 m high and about 2 m in diameter, with branches extending horizontally. Leaves ovate, ocordate and entire to oblong-obtuse and with up to six teeth in the apex, up to 8 cm long, pubescent first and later glabrous. Flowers hermaphrodite, clustered in capitulum up to 12 cm in diameter. Perianth up to 3.5 cm long. Style curved near its apex, up to 6 cm long. The perianth and style are usually orange although sometimes there are plants with yellow or red ones. Fruits are achenes, whitish.

Needs acid soil, preferably sandy-loam, with low content of salts, but well drained. Requires sunny site. Sensitive to frost. Slow growing.

Grown for its extremely beautiful flowers, very long lasting in water after cut, about two weeks, although with a floral preserver they can last four weeks or more.

In gardening used individually or in groups.

Flowering: Late winter-spring.
Propagation: By seed and cuttings.

Malvaviscus arboreus Cav. [*M. mollis* (Ait.) DC.]. Malvaceae.
Mexico to Peru and Brazil.

WAX MALLOW

Shrub evergreen, up to 3.5 m high. Leaves simple, alternate, lobulate or not, ovate to suborbicular, dentate, acuminate, densely pubescent, up to 20 cm or more. Flowers hermaphrodite, erect, usually solitary in axils of leaves. Corolla funnel-shaped, bright red, with petals convolute, about 3 cm long. Stamens joined in one tubular column longer than petals. in schizocarp.

Not particular about soil. Prefers sunny situation, although lives well in partial shade. Fast growing.

In gardening used individually, in groups and for hedges.

Flowering: Nearly year-round.
Propagation: By seed and cuttings.

Mandevilla laxa (Ruiz et Pav.) Woodson [*M. suaveolens* Lindl.]. Apocynaceae. Bolivia and northern Argentina.

JASMINE OF CHILE

Climber woody, evergreen. Leaves opposite, ovate, with cordate base, acuminate, up to 22 cm long, hairy above and glabrous beneath, except for group of hairs in the axils of side veins. Petioles up to 5.5 cm long, with reddish tint. Flowers hermaphrodite, fragrant, grouped in racemes. Calyx 5-partite. Corolla funnel-shaped, white to creamy white, 5-lobed, up to 5 cm long and 8 cm in diameter. Fruits in folioles, cylindrical, up to 50 cm long.

Not particular about soil. Prefers sunny location. Moderate growth.

Used in gardening to cover pergolas, walls, etc.

Flowering: Spring-summer.
Propagation: By seed and cuttings.

Merremia tuberosa (L.) Rendle [_Ipomoea tuberosa_ L.].
Convolvulaceae. Probably from Tropical America.

WOOD ROSE

Evergreen climber. Leaves palmatipartite, with seven segments oblong-lanceolate. Petioles long, up to 14 cm in length. Flowers hermaphrodite, tubular-funnel shaped, up to 5.5 cm in diameter. Corolla yellow. Flowers in clusters with varied number of flowers. Fruits in capsules, globose, irregularly dehiscent, which when dry, look like a rose carved in wood.

Accepts most soils. Requires sunny location. Drought-resistant. Fast growing.

Used in gardening to cover walls, fences and pergolas.

Flowering: Autumn and spring.
Propagation: By seed and cuttings.

Monstera deliciosa Liebm. [*Philodendron pertusum* Kunth et Bouché]. Araceae. Mexico and Central America.

CERIMAN

Climber woody, evergreen, with aerial roots growing along the stem. Leaves large with limb cordate-ovate, pinnatifid, perforated with holes elliptical to oblong, coriaceous, up to 70 cm long. Petioles articulate, winged, as long as limbs. Flowers very small, arranged on a cylindrical spadix up to 25 cm long surrounded by a creamy spathe, curved. Flowers hermaphrodite, fertile, in upper part and sterile ones in lower part. Fruits in berries, small, that appear grouped on an enlarged spadix forming a multiple, edible fruit.

Not particular regarding soil, although grows better in rich, well drained earth. Prefers partially shady location. Somewhat resistant to low temperatures.

Cultivated in tropics for its fruit which has a taste between pineapple and banana.

In gardening used to cover walls, columns, etc. Also to cover the ground like a carpet and as decorative potted indoor plant.

Propagation: Normally by cuttings.

Montanoa bipinnatifida (Kunth) C. Koch. Compositae. Mexico.

DAISY TREE

Shrub evergreen up to 3 m high. Leaves opposite, pinnatifid to bipinnatifid, hairy. Limbs up to 45 cm long. Petioles up to 15 cm long. Flowers clustered in fragrant capitulum up to 7 cm in diameter arranged in panicles. Disc-floret yellowish. Ligules white. Fruits in achenes.

Not particular about soil. Needs sunny site. Fast growing. Should be pruned after flowering.

Used in gardening individually or to form groups.

Flowering: Late autumn-winter-spring.
Propagation: By seed and cuttings.

Montanoa hisbiscifolia (Benth.) C. Koch. Compositae. South Mexico and from Guatemala to Costa Rica.

Shrub evergreen up to 6 m high. Leaves opposite, palmatilobed, cordate, hairy. Limbs up to 45 cm long. Petioles up to 40 cm long. Flowers clustered in fragrant capitulum up to 5 cm in diameter arranged in panicles. Disc-floret yellowish. White ligules. Fruits in achenes.

Tolerates most soils. Needs sunny site. Fast growing. Should be pruned after flowering.

Used in gardening individually or in groups.

Flowering: Late autumn-early winter.
Propagation: By seed and cuttings.

Musa rubra Wall. Musaceae. Burma.

Herb perennial, rhizomatous, with pseudostems up to 1.30 m high or more and 8 cm in diameter at base, tinted purple and black. Leaves arranged helicoidally, oblong-lanceolate, green, up to 2.30 m long, with reddish central vein, canaliculate above and prominent beneath. Flowers unisexual appearing in clusters along rachis pubescent, reddish of erect terminal spike, protected by a red bract. The females in lower part and males in upper part. Calyx with five yellow lobes. Petal shorter than calyx. Fruits in berries, yellow, up to 9 cm long.

Needs rich, well drained soil and abundant moisture. Requires sunny site although accepts some shade. Must be protected from wind. Fast growing. Each pseudostem produces a bunch of small, unedible bananas and then dies. Used in gardening to form groups.

Propagation: By seed and division.

Orthrosanthus multiflorus Sw. Iridaceae. Australia.

Herb perennial, rhizomatous. Leaves linear, similar to those of graminaceous plants, up to 55 cm long and up to 1 cm broad. Flowers blue in colour, about 3 cm in diameter, clustered in racemes arranged in panicles longer than leaves. Fruits in capsules.

Tolerates most soils. Needs shady location. Resistant to frost.

Used in gardening to form groups, in borders, etc.

Flowering: Spring.
Propagation: By seed and division.

Pandorea pandorana (Andr.) Steenis [*Bignonia pandorana* Andr.].
Bignoniaceae. Malayan Archipelago, Australia.

WONGA-WONGA VINE

Climber woody, evergreen. Leaves opposite, imparipinnate, with 3-9 folioles, up to 14 cm long. Folioles ovate to ovate-lanceolate, entire to densely crenate or dentate, up to 9 cm long, lighter beneath. Flowers hermaphrodite, clustered in terminal panicles up to 20 cm long. Corolla funnel shaped-campanulate, five-lobed, somewhat bilabiate, white with lobes and neck tinted purple, up to 19 mm long. Fruits in woody capsules.

Prefers rich, well drained soil and somewhat shady site. Resistant to frost. Fast growing.

Used in gardening to cover walls, pergolas, fences, etc.

Flowering: Winter-spring.
Propagation: By seed and cuttings.

Passiflora edulis Sims. Passifloraceae. Brazil.

PURPLE GRANADILLA, PASSION FRUIT

Climber evergreen, with stems obtusely angulous, glabrous. Leaves alternate, trilobate, glabrous, serrate, up to 20 cm long or more. Flowers hermaphrodite, solitary, in leaf axils, up to 8 cm in diameter, subtended by three serrate bracts, up to 2.5 cm long. Sepals and petals white, often with purple tints. Filaments of crown white with base tinted purple. Fruits in berries, globular-oblong, purple when ripe, up to 5-6 cm in diameter.

Prefers good quality soils, well drained. Needs sunny situation. Fast growing.

Cultivated in tropical and subtropical areas for its fruit whose pulp is eaten fresh or used in preparing juice, jams, soft drinks, etc.

In gardening it is used to cover walls, pergolas, etc.

Flowering: Late spring-summer-autumn.
Propagation: By seed and cuttings.

Passiflora mollissima (HBK) L. H. Bailey. Passifloraceae.
Venezuela to Bolivia.

BANANA PASSION FRUIT

Climber evergreen with axillary tendrils and stems dense and finely tomentose, cylindrical. Leaves alternate, three-lobed, with acute lobes and margins serrate-dentate, pubescent beneath, up to 14 cm long. Flowers hermaphrodite, solitary, in axils of leaves, up to 9 cm in diameter, subtended on three bracts. Five sepals and five petals pink in colour, joined at the base to form a tube up to 7 cm long, green. Crown is reduced to a band of purple, tuberculate. Stamen, five, joined to column bearing ovary and only separate in upper part of this column. Styles, three. Fruits in berries, oblong-ovoid, like a banana, yellow.

Prefers top quality soils with good drainage. Requires sunny site. Fast growing.

Fruit edible, giving top quality juice.

Used in gardening to cover walls, pergolas, etc.

Flowering: Nearly year-round.
Propagation: By seed and cuttings.

Passiflora trifasciata Lem. Passifloraceae. Peru.

Climber evergreen. Leaves alternate, three-lobed, up to 22 cm long. Limbs green above, with yellowish-green colour along veins, with purple tones on young leaves, and reddish to violet beneath. Flowers hermaphrodite, in groups of two in axils of leaves, up to 3.5 cm in diameter. Sepals and petals greenish white. Crown whitish, with outer ring formed by filaments arranged radially. Stamens and styles bent downwards.

Prefers fertile, well drained soils. Can live in bright sun as well as in shade. Fast growing.

Used in gardening to cover walls, etc.

Flowering: Autumn-winter.
Propagation: By seed and cuttings.

Petrea volubilis L. Verbenaceae. Central America, Mexico, West Indies.

QUEEN'S-WREATH

Climber woody or sub-shrub deciduous. Leaves opposite, entire or undulated, ovate, elliptical or oblong, acute, acuminate, obtuse or emarginated, very rough, like sand paper when mature, up to 20 cm long. Petioles short, up to 1 cm long. Flowers hermaphrodite, pale lilac to purple, up to 4 cm in diameter, clustered in racemes axillary pendulous, up to 45 cm long. Calyx same colour as corolla, but usually paler. Corolla falls off after a few days, calyx remains for a long time. Fruits in drupes.

Not particular about soil. Needs bright sun. Drought-resistant. Slow growing.

One of the most beautiful flowered climbers. Used to cover walls, pergolas, etc.

Flowering: Almost all year.
Reproduction: By seed and cuttings.

Phymosia umbellata (Cav.) Kearn. [*Sphaeralcea umbellata* (Cav.) G. Don]. Malvaceae. Mexico.

Shrub or small tree evergreen up to 6 m high. Leaves simple, palmatilobate, densely pubescent, with 3-5-7 lobes not deep, sinuate-dentate. Limbs up to 16.5 cm long. Petioles of similar length. Flowers hermaphrodite, clustered in cymes umbellate. Caliculus formed by three separate bracts. Corolla red-pink in colour, formed by five petals. Stamens joined in a tubular column. Fruits in schizocarps.

Not particular regarding soil. Prefers sunny location.

In gardening used individually or to form groups.

Flowering: Autumn-winter.
Propagation: By seed and cuttings.

Pithecoctenium echinaturm (Jacq.) K. Schum. [*P. muricatum* Mo. ex DC.]. Bignoniaceae. Cuba, Jamaica and from Mexico to Brazil and Paraguay.

MONKEY'S COMB

Climber woody, evergreen, with angulose branches. Leaves opposite, 3-foliolate or 2-foliolate with terminal foliole converted into tripartite tendril. Folioles broadly ovate to suborbicular, up to 10 cm long. Flowers hermaphrodite, clustered in racemes terminal up to 20 cm long. Corolla tubulose-funnel shaped, somewhat bilabiate, pubescent, white with yellow throat, up to 5 cm long. Tube elbowed and limb five-lobed. Fruits in capsules, muricate, spiny, up to 15 cm long.

Accepts most soils. Needs sunny location.

Used in gardening to cover pergolas, walls, etc.

Flowering: Spring.
Propagation: By seed and cuttings.

Pittosporum tobira (Thunb.) Ait. Pittosporaceae. China, Japan.

JAPANESE PITTOSPORUM

Shrub or small tree evergreen up to 5.5 m high. Leaves alternate or pseudoverticilate, obovate, with apex obtuse, coriaceous, thick, with margins revolute, dark green, glossy above and paler beneath, up to 11.5 cm long. Flowers hermaphrodite, pentamerous, fragrant, up to 2 cm in diameter, in racemes umbellate terminal. Corolla white to yellowish-white, up to 8 mm long. Fruits in capsules, ovoid or almost triangular, up to 1.5 cm long, pubescent.

Not particular about soil. Prefers sunny location. Salt-tolerant so it is recommended for coastal gardens.

Used in gardening individually, to form groups or for hedges.

Flowering: Late winter-spring.
Propagation: By seed, cuttings and grafting.

Pittosporum undulatum Venten. Pittosporaceae. Australia.

VICTORIA BOXWOOD, MOCK ORANGE

Tree evergreen up to 12 m high. Leaves alternate or pseudoverticilate, oblong to lanceolate. coriaceous, with revolute margins, undulated, dark green, glossy above and paler beneath, up to 15 cm long. Petioles short. Flowers hermaphrodite, white, fragrant, up to 15 mm in diameter, in racemes umbellate terminal. Corolla up to 8 mm long. Fruits in capsules subglobose, orange when ripe, up to 1.5 cm in diameter.

Not particular regarding soil. Prefers sunny site. Salt-tolerant so recommended for coastal gardens. Fast growing. Resistant to frost.

Used in gardening to form hedges, screens and as a shade tree.

Flowering: Late winter-spring.
Propagation: By seed and cuttings.

Plumbago auriculata. Lam. [*P. capensis* Thunb.]. Plumbaginaceae.
South Africa.

PLUMBAGO, LEADWORT

Shrub evergreen, semi-climber. Leaves alternate, entire, simple,
oblong or oblong-spathulate, up to 8.5 cm long. Flowers blue or
white, up to 4 cm long, in spikes short. Corolla salverform with long,
slender tube, and limb pentalobed, up to 3.5 cm in diameter. Fruits in
capsules.

Not demanding about soil. Needs strong sun, although tolerates
partial shade. Sensitive to frost. Somewhat drought-resistant. Fast
growing.

In South Africa some people think it has medicinal and magic
properties. Its ground root is used to cure headaches and injuries.

In gardening used to cover walls, to form hedges, etc.

Flowering: Nearly year-round.
Propagation: By seed and cuttings.

Podranea brycei (N. E. Br.) T. Sprague [*Tecoma brycei* N. E. Br.; Pandorea brycei (N. E. Br.) Rehd.]. Bignoniaceae. Zimbabwe.

QUEEN-OF-SHEBA VINE

Shrub climber evergreen. Leaves opposite, imparipinnate, up to 18 cm long, with 9-13 folioles lanceolate to ovate, glabrous, entire to serrate, acuminate, up to 8 cm long. Flowers hermaphrodite, clustered in panicles terminal. Corolla funnel shaped-campanulate, somewhat bilabiate, purple with darker strias coming out of bottom of tube, up to 6 cm long and 7.5 cm in diameter. Hairy neck same as inside tube. Fruits in capsules, linear, coriaceous, up to 40 cm long or more, containing many winged seeds.

Prefers good quality soil. Requires sunny site. Somewhat drought-resistant. Fast growing.

Used in gardening to cover fences, pergolas, etc.

Flowering: Nearly year-round.
Propagation: By seed and cuttings.

Podranea ricasoliana (Tanfani) T. Sprague [_Tecoma ricasoliana_ Tanfani; _Pandorea ricasoliana_ (Tanfani) Baill.]. Bignoniaceae. South Africa.

PINK TRUMPET VINE

Shrub climber evergreen. Leaves opposite, imparipinnate, up to 25 cm long, with 9-13 folioles ovate, serrate, glabrous, acute or acuminate, up to 10 cm long. Flowers hermaphrodite, clustered in panicles terminal. Corolla funnel shaped-campanulate, somewhat bilabiate, pink with red strias coming from bottom of tube, up to 6 cm long and 6 cm in diameter. Throat and tube slightly hairy. Fruits in capsules, linear, up to 40 cm long or more, containing many winged seeds.

Prefers good quality soil. Requires sunny site. Somewhat drought-resistant. Fast growing.

Used in gardening to cover walls, pergolas, etc.

Flowering: Nearly year-round.
Propagation: By seed and cuttings.

Polyscias guilfoylei (Bull) L. H. Bailey [*Aralia guilfoylei Bull*].
Araliaceae. Polynesia.

WILD COFFEE

Shrub evergreen, erect growing up to 6 m high. Leaves pinnate, up to 60 cm long or more. Folioles ovate to nearly orbicular, serrate, usually with margins white or yellowish, although sometimes these colours can reach other areas of limb. Foliole terminal larger, up to 20 cm long or more. Flowers small, clustered in umbels arranged in panicles (does not usually bloom when cultivated). Fruits in drupes.

Prefers rich, well drained soil. Accepts bright sun as well as shade. Drought-resistant. Fast growing.

Used in gardening individually, in groups or for hedges.

Propagation: Normally, by cuttings.

Psidium littorale Raddi **var. longipes** (O. Berg.) [*P. cattleianum* Sab.]. Myrtaceae. Brazil.

PURPLE STRAWBERRY GUANA

Shrub or small tree evergreen up to 6 m high. Bark greyish-brown. Leaves elliptical to obovate, glabrous, opposite, cuneate, up to 8 cm long. Flowers white, solitary, up to 2.5 cm in diameter. Fruits in berries, subglobose, up to 2.5 cm in diameter, red-purple in colour, edible and taste similar to strawberries.

Prefers well drained soils and abundant moisture. Needs sunny location.

Widely cultivated in tropical and subtropical areas for its fruit, which can be eaten fresh or used in making jams. Its juice is used in soft drinks.

Also planted as ornamental tree in parks and gardens.

Flowering: Spring.
Propagation: By seed, cuttings and grafting.

Pyrostegia venusta (Ker-Gawl.) Miers [*P. ignea* (Vell.) K. Presl; *Bignonia venusta* Ker-Gawl.; *B. ignea* Vell.]. Bignoniaceae. Brazil, Paraguay.

FLAME VINE

Shrub climber evergreen. Leaves opposite, composite, with 2-3 folioles. Tendrils filiform, tripartite. Folioles ovate, acuminate, up to 12 cm long. Flowers hermaphrodite, red-orange, clustered in cymes paniculate axillary and terminal. Corolla tubular-funnel shaped, curved, with reflexed lobes, up to 6 cm long. Stamens exserted in fours. Fruits in capsules, linear, up to 30 cm long.

Not particular regarding soil, prefers fertile, well drained bed. Requires sunny location. Sensitive to frost. Fast growing.

Used in gardening to cover pergolas, taluses, walls, etc.

Flowering: Nearly year-round.
Propagation: Usually by cuttings and air layering.

Quisqualis indica L. Combretaceae. Burma, Malaccan peninsula, Philippines, New Guinea.

RANGOON CREEPER

Shrub climber, woody. Leaves opposite, oblong to oblong-elliptical, acuminate, up to 12 cm long, hairy. Flowers hermaphrodite, fragrant, clustered in hanging spikes. Tube of calyx green, slender, up to 6 cm long or more. Corolla with five petals, whose outer surface is white with pink tints. The inside first is white in the morning; then changes to pink and finally is red. Fruit dry, winged, containing one seed.

Not demanding about soil. Prefers sunny location, although accepts some shade. Fast growing.

Used in gardening to cover pergolas, walls, etc.

Flowering: Late spring-summer-autumn.
Propagation: By seed, cuttings and air layering.

Raphiolepis umbellata (Thunb.) Mak [*R. japonica* Siebold et Zucc.].
Rosaceae. Japan.

YEDDA HAWTHORN

Shrub evergreen up to 3 m high. Leaves alternate, ovate-oblong to obovate, coriaceous, revolute, dark green above and paler beneath, entire to serrate, up to 9.5 cm long. Flowers white, fragrant, up to 1.5 cm in diameter, clustered in dense panicles. Fruits in pomes similar to drupes, bluish-black, subglobose, up to 9 mm long.

Prefers fertile, well drained soil. Thrives in strong sun, although it can be cultivated in shade. Slow growing.

In Japan a brown dye is obtained from the bark.

Used in gardening individually or to form groups and as potted plant.

Flowering: Nearly all year.
Propagation: By seed, cuttings and grafting.

Rhapis humilis Blume. Palmae. Southern China.

REED RHAPIS

Dioecious palm with multiple stems, similar to canes, reaching 4.5 m high or more, covered with brown fiber. Leaves palmate, divided nearly to the base in up to 24 linear segments, up to 50 cm long and 6 cm wide or more, with apex narrow, truncate and dentate. Inflorescences appear among the leaves with very small unisexual flowers. Fruits in berries.

Not demanding regarding soil. Prefers partially shaded spots, although allows planting in bright sun.

Very decorative, used in gardening to form groups and hedges. Also as indoor potted plant and in decorating patios.

Propagation: By seed and division.

Russelia equisetiformis Schlechtend. et Cham. [*R. juncea* Zucc.].
Scrophulariaceae. Mexico.

CORAL PLANT

Shrub up to 1.80 m high, with stems angulous, glabrous, graciously arched and pendulous. Leaves verticillate, linear-lanceolate to ovate, serrate, up to 2.5 cm long, reduced to scales on branches. Flowers hermaphrodite, red, clustered in cymes axillary at end of branches and stems. Corolla tubular, five-lobed, somewhat bilabiate, up to 2.5 cm long. Fruits in capsules.

Not demanding about soil. Prefers sunny situation, although can live in some shade.

Used in gardening to form groups or individually. Also as potted plant.

Flowering: Nearly year-round.
Propagation: By seed, cuttings and shoots.

Ruttya fruticosa Lindau. Acanthaceae. Tropical East Africa.

RUTTYA

Shrub evergreen up to 3.5 m high. Leaves opposite, entire, acuminate, ovate, up to 8 cm long. Flowers hermaphrodite, clustered in cymes. Calyx pentapartite. Corolla bilabiate, up to 5 cm long, with upper lip emarginated and lower one trilobate, yellow, orange-red or scarlet, with a spot in dark red, brown or black at base of middle lobe of lower lip, also affecting base of lateral lobes. Stamens, two. Fruits in capsules.

Not demanding about soil. Prefers sunny site. Fast growing.

In gardening used as individual sample or to form groups.

Flowering: Nearly year-round.
Reproduction: Usually by cuttings.

Salvia leucantha Cav. Labiatae. Mexico.

MEXICAN BUSH SAGE

Shrub evergreen up to 1.30 m high or more, with stems and branches lanate. Leaves opposite, linear-lanceolate, acute, crenate, rugose and pubescent above and lanate beneath, up to 15 cm long and 3 cm broad. Flowers hermaphrodite, clustered in racemes spiciform up to 30 cm long or more. Calyx funnel-shaped covered with violaceous pubescence. Corolla pubescent, bilabiate, up to 2 cm long, white with violaceous tones. Fruit formed by four nucules.

Prefers well drained soil. Thrives in sunny, dry places.

Usually used in gardening to form groups or carpet areas.

Flowering: Nearly all year.
Propagation: By seed and cuttings.

Senecio petasitis (Sims) DC. Compositae. Mexico.

CALIFORNIA GERANIUM

Shrub evergreen that can reach 2.5 m high or more. Branches and petioles hirsute-velutinous. Leaves alternate, ovate to suborbicular, lobate, hirsutellous above and with greyish tomentum beneath, up to 30 cm long or more, largely petiolate. Flowers in heads clustered in terminal panicles. Heads about 1.5 cm long and 2 cm in diameter, with five yellow ligules and the disc brown. Fruits in achenes, with whitish pappus.

Not demanding about soil, although prefers fertile, well drained ones. Can live in bright sun as well as in shade. Fast growing.

Used in gardening individually and to form groups.

Flowering: Winter-spring.
Propagation: By seed and cuttings.

Solandra maxima (Sessé et Moç.) P. S. Green [*S. nitida* Zuccagni; *S. hartwegii* N. E. Br.]. Solanaceae. Mexico.

GOLD CUP

Shrub climber, woody, evergreen. Leaves alternate, entire, coriaceous, elliptical, obtuse to shortly acuminate, up to 27 cm long, with long petioles. Flowers hermaphrodite, solitary in short clusters, funnel shaped. Calyx three or four-lobed, up to 10 cm long. Corolla yellow, changing to yellow-brown with age, with five broad purple strias on inside, pentalobed, with lobes ornate and reflexed, up to 20 cm long. Fruits in berries, globose.

Accepts most soils. Requires abundant water, although has certain tolerance to drought. Needs sunny location. Somewhat resistant to frost. Should be pruned to shape. Fast growing.

Used in gardening to cover pergolas, walls, etc.

Flowering: Autumn-winter-spring-early summer.
Propagation: Usually by cuttings and air layering.

Solanum seaforthianum Andr. Solanaceae. Tropical America.

Plant climber, evergreen. Leaves can run from simple to pinnatifid or pinnate, up to 7.5 cm long. Flowers blue to purple, clustered in side cymes. Corolla star-shaped, pentapartite, up to 2.5 cm in diameter. Fruits in berries, globose, scarlet in colour.

Not particular regarding soil. Can be planted in shade. Sensitive to cold.

In gardening used to cover walls, pergolas, etc.

Flowering: Nearly year-round.
Propagation: By seed and cuttings.

Solanum wendlandii Hook. F. Solanaceae. Costa Rica.

POTATO VINE

Plant climber, woody, somewhat spiny. Leaves vary in shape and size. The inside ones are pinnate; the middle ones, three-lobed or trifoliate, and the upmost ones simple, oblong-acuminate. Flowers hermaphrodite in terminal racemes. Corolla blue-lilac up to 6 cm in diameter. Fruits in berries, globose to ovoid, up to 10 cm in diameter.

Accepts most soils. Needs sunny situation and abundant watering and fertilizing. Sensitive to frost. Fast growing.

Used in gardening to cover walls, pergolas, etc.

Flowering: Late spring-summer-autumn.
Propagation: By seed and cuttings.

118

Sphaeropteris cooperi (F. J. Muell.) Tryon [*Alsophila cooperi* F. J. Muell; *Cyathea cooperi* (F. J. Muell.) Domin.]. Cyatheaceae. Australia.

AUSTRALIAN TREE FERN

Fern arborescent up to 6 m high or more, with trunk covered with scales. These do not end in a hardened hair and they have all cells similar. Fronds tripinnate up to 3 m long. Pinnas oblong-lanceolate up to 75 cm long. Pinnules serrate. Sorus rounded.

Requires soil rich in organic matter, well drained and with plenty of moisture. Accepts bright sun, although prefers sunny site. Little resistance to wind. In time of active growth, the trunk must be watered frequently. Fast growing.

Used in gardening individually or to form groups. Also as potted plant for decorating patios and interiors.

Propagation: By spores.

Strelitzia nicolai Regel et Körn. Musaceae. South Africa.

BIRD-OF-PARADISE TREE

Plant with woody trunk up to 8 m high. Leaves distichous similar to those of the banana plant, oblong, up to 3.40 long, at end of trunk. The inflorescences grow from the axils of leaves. Floral scape short, with one or two boat-shaped bracts at its end, purple, up to 40 cm long, with the flowers inside them. Flowers hermaphrodite, with sepals white and petals blue. Fruits in capsules. Seeds oblong, black, up to 1 cm long, with a filamentous aril orange in colour.

Prefers soils rich in organic matter and abundant moisture. Thrives in sunny site, although accepts some shade.

In gardening used individually or in groups.

Flowering: Nearly year-round.
Propagation: By seed, shoots and division.

Strelitzia reginae Ait. Musaceae. South Africa.

STRELITZIA, BIRD OF PARADISE

Plant herbaceous perennial, rhizomatous, acaulescent, up to 1.50 m high. Leaves oblong-lanceolate, concave, somewhat glaucous beneath, up to 1.20 m long. Floral scape longer than leaves, with one or two boat-shaped bracts at its end, green with purple or red margins, up to 22 cm long, containing the flowers. These are hermaphrodite, with three slender sepals, orange or yellow and three petals, two of which are joined to form a sagittate organ (tongue) dark blue in colour, with a central channel where there are the stamens and style. Fruits in capsules. Seeds black, somewhat globose, with filamentous orange aril.

Prefers soils rich in organic matter and with abundant moisture. Requires sunny location, although accepts some shade. Slow growing.

Used in gardening individually or to form groups. Also cultivated for cut flowers.

Flowering: Nearly year-round.
Propagation: By seed, shoot and division.

Tamarindus indica L. Leguminosae. Probably from India.

TAMARIND

Tree with persistent leaves, up to 24 m high. Leaves paripinnate, up to 13 cm long. Folioles oblong, with apex obtuse or emarginated, up to 2.5 cm long. Flowers hermaphrodite, light yellow, up to 3.5 cm in diameter, clustered in racemes terminal, with few flowers. Petals with red veins. Fruit in legumes indehiscent, oblong, flat, brown, somewhat constricted, up to 15 cm long.

Prefers rich, deep soils with abundant moisture. Susceptible to frost.

The tamarind is cultivated for its fruit, which contains a bitter, edible pulp. This pulp is used to prepare chutneys and spices, soft drinks, sweets and jams, and in medicine as it is carminative, laxative and antiscorbutic. The wood is used in carpentry.

Used a a shade tree in gardens and parks and in town alignments.

Flowering: Late summer-autumn.
Propagation: By seed, cuttings and grafting.

Tecomaria capensis (Thunb.) Spach [*Tecoma capensis* (Thunb.) Lindl.]. Bignoniaceae. South Africa.

CAPE HONEYSUCKLE

Shrub semi-climber, woody, evergreen. Leaves opposite or in groups of three, imparipinnate, up to 15 cm long. Folioles serrate, elliptical to ovate, orbicular or rhomboidal, up to 5.5 cm long. Flowers hermaphrodite, red-orange to scarlet, up to 5.5 cm long, clustered in racemes terminal. Fruits in capsules, linear, up to 5 cm long.

Not particular about soil, although grows better in rich ones with adequate moisture. Drought resistant. Prefers sunny spots. Fast growing.

Used to cover walls, pergolas, etc. and to form hedges. Regular pruning keeps it shrub-shaped.

Flowering: Nearly year-round.
Propagation: By seed, cuttings and air layering.

Tetrapanax papyriferus (Hook.) C. Koch [*Fatsia papyrifera* (Hook.)
Benth et Hook. f.]. Araliaceae. China and Taiwan.

RICE PAPER PLANT

Shrub to small tree evergreen, stoloniferous, inermous, up to 6 m
high. Leaves more or less verticillate, palmatilobate, with lobes
serrate, cordate-ovate, densely pubescent beneath. Limbs up to
85 cm long. Petioles up to 95 cm long or more. Flowers
hermaphrodite, small, white, arranged in umbels grouped in a
panicle terminal lanate more than 1 m long. Fruits in drupes,
globular.

Not demanding about soil. Requires shady situation. Fast
growing.

Cultivated in the Orient for manufacture of rice paper made with
thin sheets obtained from the pith of the stems.

Used in gardening to form groups.

Flowering: Autumn-early winter.
Propagation: By seed, shoots and root cuttings.

Thunbergia coccinea Wallich. Acanthaceae. India.

Plant climber woody, evergreen. Leaves opposite, thick, glabrous, ovate to oblong, with base cordate or angular, dentate, dark green above and a little glaucous beneath, acuminate, up to 24 cm long. Flowers hermaphrodite, subtended by two large purple bracts, clustered in racemes pendulous up to 50 cm long. Corolla up to 2.5 cm long, with five lobes reflexed, scarlet and yellow throat. Fruits in capsules.

Prefers good quality, well drained soils. Requires sunny location.

Used in gardening to cover walls, pergolas, etc.

Flowering: Autumn-winter-spring.
Propagation: By seed, cuttings and air layering.

Thunbergia grandiflora (Roxb. ex Rottl.) Roxb. Acanthaceae. India.

BLUE TRUMPET VINE

Climbing plant, woody, evergreen. Leaves opposite, broadly ovate, rough, with margins dentate or angularly lobed, palmativeined, with 5-7 veins. Petioles up to 6.5 cm long. Limbs up to 20 cm long. Flowers hermaphrodite blue, solitary or usually clustered in racemes pendulous. Corolla up to 7.5 cm in diameter, with five lobes rounded, somewhat bilabiate. Tube up to 3.5 cm long, with yellow throat. Fruits in capsules.

Grows better in good quality soil with easy drainage. Prefers sunny location. Fast growing. Somewhat resistant to cold.

Used in gardening to cover walls, fences, pergolas, etc.

Flowering: Nearly year-round.
Propagation: Usually by cuttings.

Zantedeschia aethiopica (L.) K. Spreng. [*Richardia africana* Kunth]. Araceae. South Africa.

CALLA LILY

Plant herbaceous, acaulescent, rhizomatous, up to 90 cm high or more. Leaves entire, sagittate, with cordiform base. Petioles long. Limbs green, glossy, up to 45 cm long and 25 cm broad. Flowers unisexual, small arranged along a cylindrical spadix yellow in colour, the male ones in the upper part and females ones in lower part. Spathe white, funnel-shaped, with short tube and curved limb, up to 25 cm long. Floral scape surpasses height of leaves. Fruits in berries.

Prefers rich soil with abundant moisture. Thrives when cultivated in partially shady spot. Fast growing.

The first South African settlers used it to treat gout and rheumatism.

Very popular in gardening to form groups, bordering ponds and as water plants. Also used for cut flowers.

Flowering: Nearly year-round.
Propagation: By seed and division.

BIBLIOGRAPHY

GLOSSARIES

INDEXES

BIBLIOGRAPHY

BAILEY, L. H.: *The Standard Cyclopedia of Horticulture*, 3 vols., 3 639 p., The MacMillan Company, Nueva York, 1947.

CHITTENDEN, F. J. (Ed.): *The Royal Horticultural Society Dictionary of Gardening*, 3 vols., 2 316 p., Oxford University Press. Oxford, 1977.

— *Supplement to the Royal Horticultural Society Dictionary of Gardening.* 1 088 p., Oxford University Press, Oxford, 1979.

ELIOVSON, S.: *Shrubs, Trees and Climbers for Southern Africa*, 270 p., Mac Millan South Africa, Johannesburg, 1981.

— *Wild Flowers of Southern Africa*, 310 p., Mac Millan South Africa, Johannesburg, 1984.

FONT QUER, P.: *Diccionario de Botánica*, 1 244 p., Editorial Labor, S. A., Barcelona, 1977.

GRAF, A. B.: *Exotica 3. Pictorial Cyclopedial of Exotic Plants*, 1 834 p., Roehrs Company, E. Rutheford, 1970.

— *Tropica. Color Cyclopedia of Exotic Plants and Trees*, 1 136 p., Roehrs Company, E. Rutheford, 1981.

HOYOS, J.: *Flora Tropical Ornamental*, 430 p., Sociedad de Ciencias Naturales La Salle. Monografía núm. 24, Caracas, 1978.

KUCK, L. E., y TONGG, R. C.: *The Modern Tropical Garden*, 250 p., Tongg Publishing Company, Honolulú, 1970.

KUNKEL, G.: *Flowering Trees in Subtropical Gardens*, 346 p., Dr. W. Junk b.v., Publishers, La Haya, 1978.

LIBERTY HYDE BAILEY HORTORIUM: *Hortus Third*, 1 290 p., Mac Millan Publishing Co., Inc., Nueva York, 1978.

McCURRACH, J.C.: *Palms of the World*, 290 p., Harper and Brothers, Nueva York, 1960.

MENNINGER, E.A.: *Flowering Trees of the World*, 336 p., Hearthside Press Incorporated, Nueva York, 1962.

— *Flowering Vines of the World*, 410 p., Hearthside Press Incorporated, Nueva York, 1970.

MOORE, H.E.: *The Major Groups of Palms and Their Distribution*, 115 p., L.H. Bailey Hortorium, Nueva York, 1973.

PALMER, E., y PITMAN, N.: *Trees of Southern Africa*, 3 vols., 2 235 p., A.A. Balkema, Ciudad del Cabo, 1972.

PAÑELLA BONASTRE, J.: *Árboles de Jardín,* 300 p., Oikos-tau, S. A., ediciones, Barcelona, 1972.

VAN DER SPUY, U.: *South African Shrubs and Trees for the Garden,* 215 p., Hugh Keartland Publishers, Johannesburg, 1971.

WHITMORE, T.C.: *Palms of Malaya,* 129 p., Oxford, University Press, Oxford, 1979.

WRIGLEY, J. W., y FAGG, M.: *Australian Native Plants,* 448 p., Williams Collins Publishers Pty Ltd, Sidney, 1979.

GLOSSARY OF BOTANICAL TERMS

Above.—Upper side of leaves, opposite of beneath.

Acaulescent.—Having stem so short it is practically inexistent.

Acuminate.—Ending in a point.

Acute.—Any foliaceous organ (leaf, foliole, etc.) whose edges form an acute angle at the apex.

Adaxial.—Surface nearest main axis.

Amplexicaul.—Applied to bracts, leaves, etc., completely clasping or embracing the stem.

Angulous.—Having angles.

Anther.—Pollen-producing part of the stamen.

Apetalous.—Without petals.

Apiculate.—Ending in a short, sharp pointed tip.

Achene.—A dry fruit, indehiscent, monospermous.

Aril. Excrescence of variable growth covering fully or partially the seed's surface.

Articulated.—Refers to organs with visible articulations or divisions.

Axil.—Upper angle that a lateral organ (leaf, bract, etc.) forms with the caulinar axis where inserted.

Axillary.—Situated in the axil.

Beneath.—Opposite of above in leaves, etc.

Berry.—Pulpy, indehiscent fruit containing few or many seeds, with no true stone. For example, the grape.

Bipinnate.—Twice pinnate.

Bipinnatifid.—Refers to the pinnatifid leaf whith pinnatifid divisions.

135

Bract.—A foliaceous organ, different from the leaf, associated with the flower or inflorescence.

Calyculus.—Verticil of leaves similar to sepals subtending a calyx or involucre calycine.

Calyx.—Exterior verticil of the perianth; formed by sepals.

Canaliculate.—Channeled, with one or several small channels.

Capitulum.—Inflorescence made up of sessile flowers on a very short and broad axis.

Capsule.—A dry, dehiscent fruit formed by the union of two or more carpels.

Cincinnus.—Scorpoid cyme in which the twigs it consists of grow to the right and left alternatively.

Cone.—Inflorescence formed by a central axis on which there are flowers, unisexual and bare, and the bracts. Characteristic of the coniferae (pines, firs, etc.).

Connivent.—Refers to organs touching in their upper part.

Convolute.—Rolled up lengthwise.

Cordate.—Synonym of cordiform.

Cordiform.—Heart-shaped.

Corolla.—Internal verticil of the perianth, formed by petals.

Corolline.—Similar to the corolla or characteristic of it.

Crenate.—Scalloped.

Crown.—Groups of petaloid appendages appearing between stamen and corolla.

Crownshaft.—In palms, extension of stem longer than the inflorescence, formed by the sheaths of the leaves.

Cultivar.—Cultivated variety. Group of cultivated plants easily distinguishable by morphologic, physiologic, etc. characters, and that when reproduced sexually or asexually, keep their characteristics.

Cuneate.—Wedge-shaped.

Cup-shaped.—Refers to a trumpet-shaped corolla with a long, narrow tube and open limb.

Cyme.—Defined inflorescence whose axis ends in a flower, like the lateral secondary axes.

Deciduous.—With shedding leaves.

Decurrent.—With base prolonged downwards on stem or petiole.

Dehiscent.—Fruit that opens.

Deltoid.—Triangular.

Dentate.—Refers to foliaceous organs (leaves, petals, etc.) having margins similar to a saw edge, but with less acute teeth.

Dichotomous.—Refers to branching that gives birth to two equal parts.

Dioecious.—Refers to plants with unisexual flowers (the masculine and feminine ones) on different plants.

Distichous.—Arranged in two vertical rows.

Drupe.—A pulpy fruit, monocarpelar, indehiscent, with one stone on the inside.

Emarginated.—Having a notch at the end.

Emetic.—Related with vomiting.

Ensiform.—Sword-shaped.

Evergreen.—With perennial leaves.

Exserted.—Protruding, as stamens beyond the floral parts.

Filaceous.—With threads or filaments.

Filament.—Sterile part of the stamen holding the anther.

Foliole.—Foliar organ joined to the rachis of a leaf or its divisions.

Follicle.—Dry fruit, dehiscent, monocarpelar, opening only along the ventral suture.

Fusiform.—Spindle-shaped.

Glabrous.—Without hairs.

Glaucous—Bluish-green in colour.

Gynophore.—Prolonged portion of the flower's axis situated between the androecium and gynaeceum.

Hermaphrodite.—Bisexual.

Hirsute.—Covered with long, rigid and rough hairs.

Imparipinnate.—Pinnate leaf ending in a foliole.

Indehiscent.—Does not open.

Inermous.—Without thorns nor spines.

Inflorescence.—Groups of flowers arranged in a certain characteristic way for each plant.

Infundibuliform.—Funnel-shaped.

Involute.—Refers to the leaf, foliole, etc., rolled in from the edges.

Lanceolate.—Lance-shaped.

Legume.—Dry fruit, dehiscent, monocarpelar, opening along the ventral suture and central vein, characteristic of the leguminosae.

Ligule.—Gamopetalous corolla of peripheric flowers or of all the inflorescence in the composite family.

Limb.—Laminal part of the leaf.

Linear.—Long and narrow with margins more or less parallel.

Lobate.—Lobed.

Monoecious.—Refers to plants with unisexual flowers (male and female) on same plant.

Mucronate.—Refers to any organ ending in a short point.

Multi-carpel drupe.—Drupe with more than one carpel, either with several stones or only one.

Muricate.—With thorns, needles or spines.

Nutlet.—Each of the small stones of a multi-carpel drupe.

Obcordiform.—Refers to any leaf, foliole, etc., heart-shaped, with the broadest part in the apex.

Oblanceolate.—Refers to the laminar organs (leaves, petals, etc.) that are lance-shaped upside down, with broadest part above the middle and narrowing towards the base.

Obovate.—Egg-shaped, but with broadest part towards the apex.

Obtuse.—Refers to foliar organ (bract, leaf, etc.) whose margins form an obtuse angle in the apex.

Orbicular.—Circular.

Ovate.—Oval.

Ovoid.—Egg-shaped.

Palmatilobate.—Foliaceous organ with palmate veins, divided up to middle into very marked, more or less rounded lobes.

Palmatipartite.—When the divisions reach further than the middle of the limb.

Palmatisect.—Refers to leaves, folioles, etc. with palmate veins, when their divisions reach their base.

Panicle.—A branching raceme.

Paniculate.—Arranged in panicles.

Pappus.—On certain fruit, various tufts of hairs, bristles, etc., coming out of the limb of the calyx. Also applied to tricomes appearing in the apex of certain seeds.

Paripinnate.—Refers to pinnate leaf with even number of folioles.

Peduncle.—Stalk of a flower or inflorescence.

Pentamerous.—Formed by five parts or members.

Perianth.—Floral cover. Usually formed by the calyx and corolla.

Petal.—Each of the leaves making up the corolla.

Petiole.—Stalk joining the limb of the leaf to the stem.

Pinna.—Primary foliole on a pinnate leaf.

Pinnate.—With parts (veins, folioles, etc.) arranged along both sides of the rachis in a feather-like fashion.

Pinnatifid.—Refers to the leaf, folicle, etc. with pinnate veins and divisions reaching the middle of the semi-limb.

Pinnule.—In a pinnate leaf, secondary, terciary folicle.

Pome.—Pulpy fruit, indehiscent, from a syncarpous, inferior ovary.

Puberulent.—With very few fine, short hairs.

Pubescent.—Covered with soft, short and fine hairs.

Raceme.—Inflorescence formed by a rachis with pedunculate flowers on both sides.

Rachis.—Axis of an inflorescence or of a composite leaf.

Reflexed.—Rolling backwards.

Revolute.—Refers to the leaf whose margins are rolled towards its backside.

Sagittate.—Arrow-shaped.

Salverform.—A corolla of which the tube is long and slender, and the limb flat.

Scandent.—Climber.

Scape.—Leafless stem with flowers in its apex, grows from a bulb, rhizome, etc.

Schizocarp.—Dry fruit, dehiscent, which when ripe, separates into mericarps.

Scorpoid cryme.—Refers to cyme on which its branches grow alternately to the left and right.

Sepal.—Each of the calyx's leaves.

Serrate.—Refers to foliaceous organs having margins with sharp, close teeth similar to a saw.

Sheath.—Widening of the base of the leaf which totally or partially wraps around the stem or branch it is on.

Sheathing.—Forming a sheath.

Shoot.—A new stem grown by the plant.

Sinuate.—With a wavy margin.

Sorus.—Group of sporangium on ferns.

Spadix.—Spike with pulpy rachis, generally unisexual flowers and surrounded by a spathe.

Spathe.—Bract, sometimes large and coloured, surrounding a spadix.

Spathulate.—Spoon-shaped.

Spiciform.—In spikes.

Spike.—Racemose inflorescence, simple with sessile flowers.

Stamen.—Organ of the flower with pollen sacs.

Staminode.—Sterile stamen. so-

metimes modified in shape of petal or nectary.

Standard.—Upper petal of te papilionaceous corolla.

Stoloniferous.—Produces stolons.

Subulate.—Awl-shaped.

Syconium.—Fruit of plants in the Ficus genus. It is an infrutescence composed of a pulpy receptacle containing small fruit.

Tepal.—Each of the parts of a perianth not differentiated into sepals and petals.

Tomentum.—Group of entwined hairs, fuzz-like.

Tomentose.—With tomentum.

Umbel.—Racemose inflorescence at whose end there are the pedicels of the flowers, all the same length.

Umbellate.—With umbels.

Umbelliform.—Umbel-shaped.

Unisexual.—Having one sole sex.

Utricle.—Dry fruit, indehiscent, inflated or with a membrane covering.

Velutinous.—Finely velveted.

Variegated.—Of different colours or diverse constitution.

Verticil.—Group of two or more organs (leaves, branches, etc.) all growing at same level.

Verticillate.—Arranged in verticils.

Winged.—Having a wing or wings.

Unisexual.—Con un solo sexo.

Utrículo.—Fruto seco, indehiscente, inflado o con una cubierta membranosa.

Vaina.—Ensanchamiento de la base de la hoja que envuelve total o parcialmente al tallo o rama en que se inserta.

Variegado, a.—De distintos colores o de diversa constitución.

Velutino, a.—Aterciopelado finamente.

Verticilo.—Conjunto de dos o más órganos (hojas, ramas, etc.) que salen todos al mismo nivel.

Verticilado, a.—Dispuesto en verticilo.

Vilano.—En ciertos frutos, conjunto de cerdas, pelos, etc., que proceden del limbo del cáliz. También se aplica al conjunto de tricomas que aparecen en el ápice de ciertas semillas.

ALPHABETICAL INDEX OF SCIENTIFIC NAMES

ALPHABETICAL INDEX OF FAMILIES

EUPHORBIACEAE
Acalypha hispida, 6.
Acalypha wilkesiana, 7.
Breynia disticha, 24.

IRIDACEAE
Orthrosanthus multiflorus, 88.

LABIATAE
Salvia leucantha, 114.

LEGUMINOSAE
Calliandra haematocephala, 36.
Dichrostachys cinerea ssp. cinerea, 49.
Erythrina caffra, 54.
Tamarindus indica, 124.

LYTHRACFAE
Cuphea ignea, 48.

MALVACEAF
Goethea strictiflora, 62.
Malvaviscus arboreus, 79.
Phymosia umbellata, 94.

MORACEAE
Ficus auriculata, 56.
Ficus pumila, 57.

MUSACEAE
Heliconia bihai, 66.
Musa rubra, 87.
Strelitzia nicolai, 121.
Strelitzia reginae, 122.

MYRTACEAE
Psidium littorale var. longipes, 105.

NYCTAGYNACEAE
Bougainvillea X buttiana, 'Mrs.
Butt', 16.
Bougainvillea glabra 'Sanderiana', 17.
Bougainvillea spectabilis, 18.
Bougainvillea spectabilis Cv. Lateritia, 19.

OLEACEAE
Jasminum azoricum, 73.
Jasminum mesnyi, 74.
Jasminum polyanthum, 75.

PALMAE
Brahea armata, 22.
Caryota mitis, 38.
Dictyosperma album, 50.
Rhapis humilis, 110.

PASSIFLORACEAE
Passiflora edulis, 90.
Passiflora mollissima, 91.
Passiflora trifasciata, 92.

PITTOSPORACEAE
Pittosporum tobira, 98.
Pittosporum undulatum, 100.

PROTCACEAE
Leucospermum cordifolium, 78.

PLUMBAGINACEAE
Plumbago auriculata, 101.

RHAMNACEAE
Colletia cruciata, 43.

RUBIACEAE
Gardenia cornuta, 58.
Gardenia thunbergia, 60.

ROSACEAE
Raphiolepis umbellata, 108.

INDEX OF SUBJECT MATTER

THE CANARY ISLANDS